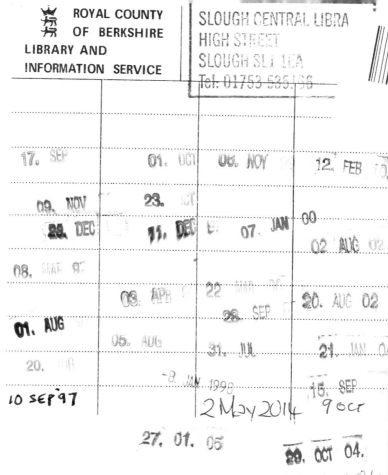

THE FORTIES

PART THREE

Production: Stephen Clark and Sadie Cook

Published 1994

ANOTHER OPENIN', ANOTHER SHOW

Words and Music by
COLE PORTER

1187

3

BLESS 'EM ALL

Words by FRANK LAKE
Music by JIMMY HUGHES

BUSY DOIN' NOTHING

Words by JOHNNY BURKE
Music by JAMES VAN HEUSEN

Last time to Coda ⊕

10

BUTTONS AND BOWS

Words and Music by
JAY LIVINGSTON and RAY EVANS

COME RAIN OR COME SHINE

Words by JOHNNY MERCER
Music by HAROLD ARLEN

16

DEAR HEARTS AND GENTLE PEOPLE

See page 20 for
Introduction and Verse

Words by BOB HILLIARD
Music by SAMMY FAIN

INTRODUCTION AND VERSE

CLOPIN CLOPANT

Words by PIERRE DUDAN
English Lyrics by KERMIT GOELL
Music by BRUNO COQUARTRIX

FIVE MINUTES MORE

See page 26 for
Introduction and Verse

Words by SAMMY CAHN
Music by JULE STYNE

INTRODUCTION AND VERSE

DAY BY DAY

Words and Music by SAMMY CAHN,
AXEL STORDAHL and PAUL WESTON

GOLDEN EARRINGS

See page 32 for
Introduction and Verse

Words by JAY LIVINGSTON and RAY EVANS
Music by VICTOR YOUNG

REFRAIN
Medium Slow (*with expression*)

There's a sto-ry the gyp-sies know is true, That when your love wears gold-en ear-rings {he/she} be-longs to you. An old love sto-ry that's known to ve-ry few, But if you wear these gold-en ear-rings love will come to you.

INTRODUCTION AND VERSE

Medium Slow (*with expression*)

One day a gyp-sy showed me gold - en ear-rings, That he

wished to sell._____ They had that look of rare and

old - en ear-rings, and he swore they'd bring a magic spell._____

Back to Refrain

IT CAN'T BE WRONG

Words by KIM GANNON
Music by MAX STEINER

I COULDN'T SLEEP A WINK LAST NIGHT

See page 38 for
Introduction and Verse

Words by HAROLD ADAMSON
Music by JIMMY McHUGH

REFRAIN Slowly (with much expression)

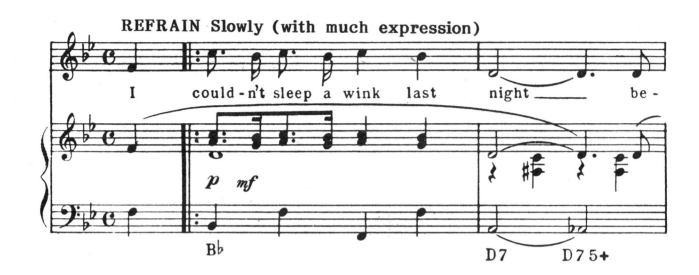

Moderato

Verse

Af-ter we part -ed last night I stayed a-wake and thought of

you; Some-how it did - n't seem right, that

you and I were real-ly through.— I thought of all the foolish things we

said, and then I just could-n't wait till I could see you a - gain.—

Back to Refrain

I'M GOING TO GET LIT-UP
(WHEN THE LIGHTS GO UP IN LONDON)

Words and Music by
HUBERT GREGG

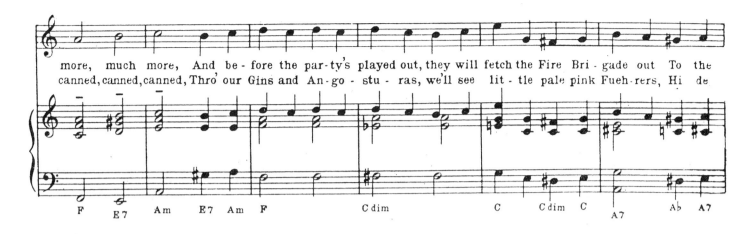

more, much more, And be-fore the par-ty's played out, they will fetch the Fire Bri-gade out To the
canned, canned, canned, Thro' our Gins and An-go-stu-ras, we'll see lit-tle pale pink Fueh-rers, Hi de

F E7 Am E7 Am F Cdim C Cdim C A7 Ab A7

lit-test-up-pest scene you ev-er saw._____ I'm going to get saw._____
Heil-ing from the Cir-cus to the Strand._____ I'm going to get Strand._____

D7 G7 F G7 C C7 Cdim Fm6 C G7 C C7 Cdim Fm6 C

ADDITIONAL CHORUSES

3.

A regular flare-up when they light Trafalgar Square up,
A regular sight to open Nelson's other eye,
Through the day and through the night,
Signal beacons they will light,
"England this day expects the nation to be tight."
They'll have to stop traffic when they light Trafalgar Square up,
And down the rocky road to Westminster we'll reel, reel, reel,
What a shindy we will kick up,
Old Big Ben will chime a hiccup,
To epitomise the sentiments we feel.

4.

I'm going to get unsedately so serenely stinking
I'm going to get stinking as I've never been before,
When the dogs have had their day,
And the fight has had its fray,
We'll all be swapping battle-dress for bottle dress that day.
I'm going to get positively permanently pie-eyed,
The day we finally exterminate the Huns, Huns, Huns,
There'll be joy and there'll be laughter,
And there'll be no Morning After,
For we'll all be drunk for muns and muns and muns.

I COULD WRITE A BOOK

Words by LORENZ HART
Music by RICHARD RODGERS

45

IF I SHOULD FALL IN LOVE AGAIN

Words and Music by
JACK POPPLEWELL

CHORUS

If I SHOULD FALL IN LOVE A-GAIN, I'd fall in love with you a-gain, With the same old

Eb   Cm   Fm   Bb7   Eb   Cm   Fm   Bb7   Eb

moon a-bove____ And your hand in mine I'd whis-per, "I love you." If I should

Eb dim   Fm   Bb7   Eb   C7   Fm   B7+ Bb7+   Eb

lose my heart a-gain, I'd choose you from the start a-gain, I'd be just the same, If I

Cm   Fm   Bb7   Eb   Cm   Fm   Bb7   Eb   D7

loved a-gain, I should still fall in love with you.____ If love with you.____

G7   C7   F9   Fm   Bb7 Eb   Dim Bb7   Bb7   Eb Dim Bb7 Eb

I HAD THE CRAZIEST DREAM

Words by MACK GORDON
Music by HARRY WARREN

49

I'M GOING TO SEE YOU TODAY

Words by JOYCE GRENFELL
Music by RICHARD ADDINSELL

I CAN'T BEGIN TO TELL YOU

See page 56 for
Introduction and Verse

Words by MACK GORDON
Music by JAMES V MONACO

INTRODUCTION AND VERSE

I nev-er have a dream, that I don't see you in it. You

nev-er leave my thoughs, no, not ev-en for a minute And if you should ask me how

deep-ly I a-dore you, I would simply re - ply;

IT'S A PITY TO SAY "GOODNIGHT"

Words and Music by
BILLY REID

58

IT COULD HAPPEN TO YOU

See page 62 for
Introduction and Verse

Words by JOHNNY BURKE
Music by JIMMY VAN HEUSEN

REFRAIN (Slowly with expression)

Hide your heart from sight, Lock your dreams at night, It could hap-pen to you. _____ Don't count stars or you might stum - ble; _____ Some - one drops a sigh, and down you tum - ble, Keep an eye on Spring,

Run when church bells ring, It could hap-pen to you._____ All I did was won-der How your arms would be, And it hap-pened to me! me!

Do you be - lieve in charms and spells, In mys-tic words and

mag-ic wands and wish - ing wells? Don't look so wise, Don't show your

scorn, Watch your - self, I warn you.

Back to Refrain

IT'S MAGIC

Words by SAMMY CAHN
Music by JULE STYNE

REFRAIN *(legato)*

You sigh, the song be-gins, You speak and I hear vi - o - lins, It's Mag - ic.____

The stars de-sert the skies and rush to nes-tle in your eyes, It's Mag - ic.____ With-out a

gold - en wand____ or mys-tic charms_____ Fan - tas - tic

things be-gin when I am in your arms.____

IT'S BEEN A LONG, LONG TIME

See page 68 for
Introduction and Verse

Words by SAMMY CAHN
Music by JULE STYNE

REFRAIN (Slow with a lift)

Just kiss me once, then kiss me twice, Then kiss me once a-gain,_ It's been a

F   Fmaj7   F6

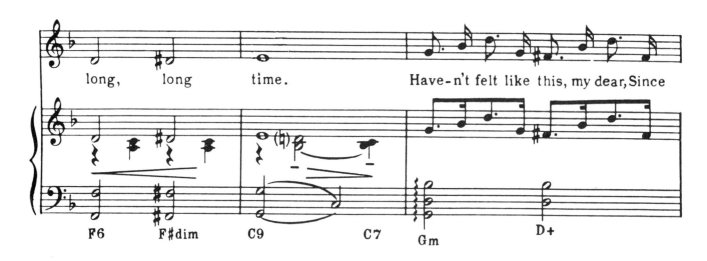

long, long time.   Have-n't felt like this, my dear, Since

F6   F#dim   C9   C7   Gm   D+

can't re-mem-ber when,_ It's been a long, long

Gm7   C7   Gm7   C9+

I'VE GOT A GAL IN KALAMAZOO

Words by MACK GORDON
Music by HARRY WARREN

LONDON PRIDE

Words and Music by
NOEL COWARD

74

76

NANCY (WITH THE LAUGHING FACE)

Words by PHIL SILVERS
Music by JIMMY VAN HEUSEN

MADEMOISELLE DE PARIS

Words by HENRI CONTET
English Lyrics by ERIC MASCHWITZ
Music by PAUL DURAND

2. Mais le cœur d'une enfant de Paris
    C'est pareil aux bouquets de violettes
    On l'attache au corsage un sam'di,
    Le dimanche on le perd à la fête.
    Adieu guinguette, adieu garçon,
    La voilà seule avec sa peine,
    Et recommence la semaine,
    Et recommence la chanson.

2. She has clothes with a zing! to 'em,
    She's got curves and they cling to 'em,
    Sheer silk stockings and shoes number three.
    Ma'moiselle de Paree.
    When she frowns there's disdain in it,
    But her smile has champagne in it,
    She breaks hearts and collects the debris
    Ma'moiselle de Paree.
    Oh! la la, Ah! oui oui,
    So you'd better look out in Paree.

Ell' chante un air de son faubourg
Ell' rêve à des serments d'amour
Ell' pleure et plus souvent qu'à son tour
Mad'moisell' de Paris.
Ell' donne un peu de ses vingt ans
Pour faire un' collection d' printemps
Et seul' s'en va rêver sur un banc
Mad'moisell' de Paris,
Trois p'tits tours,
Un bonjour
Elle oublie qu'elle a pleuré d'amour.

Ell' chante et son cœur est heureux
Ell' rêve et son rêve est tout bleu
Ell' pleur' mais ça n'est pas bien sérieux
Mad'moisell' de Paris.
Ell' vole à petits pas pressés,
Ell' court vers les Champs Elysées
Et donne un peu de son déjeuner
Aux moineaux des Tuil'ries,
Ell' fredonne,
Ell' sourit...
Et voilà Mad'moisell' de Paris.

OH! WHAT IT SEEMED TO BE

Words and Music by BENNIE BENJAMIN,
GEORGE WEISS and FRANKIE CARLE

SKYLINER

Composed by
CHARLIE BARNET

PEDRO, THE FISHERMAN

Words by HAROLD VOUSDEN PURCELL
Music by HARRY PARR-DAVIES

STELLA BY STARLIGHT

Words by NED WASHINGTON
Music by VICTOR YOUNG

SUNDAY, MONDAY, OR ALWAYS

See page 98 for
Introduction and Verse

Words by JOHNNY BURKE
Music by JIMMY VAN HEUSEN

INTRODUCTION AND VERSE

THERE MUST BE A WAY

Words and Music by SAMMY GALLOP,
DAVID SAXON and ROBERT COOK

100

SWINGING ON A STAR

See page 104 for
Introduction and Verse

Words by JOHNNY BURKE
Music by JIMMY VAN HEUSEN

REFRAIN *(With a lilt)*

INTRODUCTION AND VERSE

TWILIGHT TIME

Words and Music by BUCK RAM,
MORTY NEVINS, AL NEVINS and ARTIE DUNN

THE THINGS WE DID LAST SUMMER

See page 110 for
Introduction and Verse

Words by SAMMY CAHN
Music by JULE STYNE

INTRODUCTION AND VERSE

Slowly

mf

molto rit.

ad lib.

The weeks go quick-ly by when hearts are gay; They seem to

mp

C   Cm Cdim   G   Gdim

fly a-way, too soon they're gone. Through-out the lone-ly nights how

D9   G   Em   F#7

hard you try To lose the mem-o-ries that lin-ger on.

rit.

Bm   Gm   D   A7   D9 D7

YOU MAKE ME FEEL SO YOUNG

Words by MACK GORDON
Music by JOSEF MYROW

WHEN APRIL SINGS

Words by ERNST MARISCHKA
English Lyrics by GUS KAHN
Music by ROBERT STOLZ

YOU DON'T HAVE TO TELL ME (I KNOW)

Words and Music by
HARRY LEON and DON PELOSI

YOU'RE BREAKING MY HEART

Words and Music by
PAT GENARO and SUNNY SKYLAR

TO EACH HIS OWN

See page 122 for
Introduction and Verse

Words and Music by
JAY LIVINGSTON and RAY EVANS

Printed in Great Britain by Hobbs the Printers of Southampton 12/94